MY PROFILE

Kick off by creating your very own player profile. Then design your own shirt, using your favourite colours.

NAME: Ross Whitford

AGE: 7

TEAM I PLAY FOR: Nelson Rangers

POSITION: Striker

FAVOURITE PLAYER: Ross Whitford

FAVOURITE CLUB TEAM: Nelson Rangers

FAVOURITE INTERNATIONAL TEAM: Scotland

SHIRT:

MY AUTOGRAPH:

BEST BADGE

Whether club or country, each team has its own crest on the kit – you'll see plenty of pros in badge-kissing goal celebrations! Use the grid as a guide to copy **THE DAVID BECKHAM ACADEMY** logo into the box below.

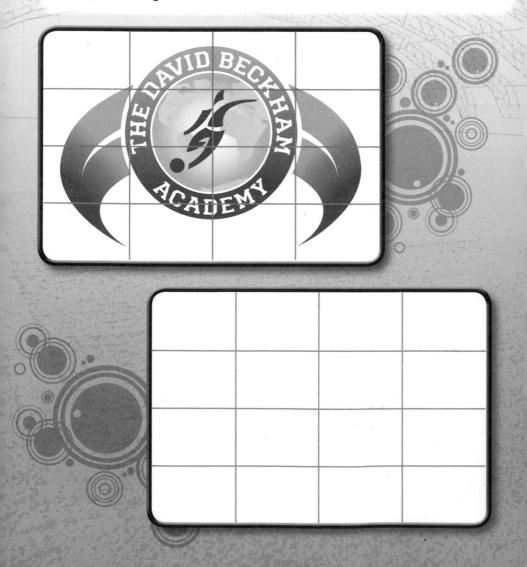

THE TEAM:

Football legends would never reach superstar status without help from the other ten on the pitch. Each player has their own important job to do, from the 'keeper to the goal-hungry strikers.

It's often the strikers that get all the glory, but every good team needs a top 'keeper between the posts. A number-one goalie must be brave, organised, good at catching and throwing, and able to stay alert in case of quick counter-attacks.

Write the name of your world-beating 'keeper here:

....

ORGANISED

BRAVE

AGILE GOALKEEPERS

Whether a wing-back, sweeper, or central defender, you have to be good at tackling and strong in the air if you want to play in defence. A defender's main job is to spot where the danger is likely to come from when the opposition is on the attack, and keep the ball away from goal.

Write the name of your greatest defender here:

....

TACKLING

STRONG

DEFENDERS

SOLID

Midfielders are often called the 'engine' of the team – which means they cover a lot of ground over 90 minutes. Energy and stamina are characteristics of great midfielders, as well as being comfortable on the ball and awesome at passing and tackling.

Write the name of your classiest midfielder here:

....

ENGINE

ENERGY

MOVE

PASS

MIDFIELDERS

All sorts of different qualities make up a good striker, from lightning-quick pace to strength and power. Strikers create chances by moving away from defenders and keeping cool in front of goal to provide a deadly finish. Top strikers need to be a bit selfish and snap up the chance to score when it comes.

Write the name of your strongest striker here:

....

STRENGTH

POWER

SPEED

STRIKERS

The man in black and his assistants are in charge of making sure the game is played fairly by both teams. If a decision doesn't go your way, keep your head up and concentrate on playing well for the rest of the game. Don't risk a yellow card or silly sending-off by arguing with the ref . . . show him some respect.

RESPECT

FAIR PLAY

REFEREES

FIVE-A-SIDE

Play this game with a team-mate or a friend. You will need a stopwatch and a coin. Toss the coin to see who will answer their questions first. Use the stopwatch to time how long it takes your opponent to answer all five questions. If you both get the same number of questions right, the quickest player wins!

PLAYER 1

	true	false
a. Extra time lasts 15 minutes.		✓
b. David Beckham captained England over 50 times.	✓	
c. The start of a game is called kick-off.	✓	
d. Two yellow cards for the same player equals a red card.	✓	
e. A penalty kick is taken from the centre circle.		✓

TIME TAKEN:

Draw in your time above.

PLAYER 2

		true	false
a.	Goalies can use their hands to receive a back-pass.	☑	☐
b.	Half-time in a pro game is after 20 minutes.	☐	☑
c.	David Beckham has earned over 100 caps for England.	☐	☑
d.	Sub is short for substitute.	☑	☐
e.	Another name for 'captain' is 'skipper'.		

TIME TAKEN:

88:88

Draw in your time above.

FINAL SCORE

PLAYER 1 | 1 | — | 0 | **PLAYER 2**

DREAM TEAM

Choose your favourite position on the pitch, then pick ten top team-mates to build the best team in the world! You could choose friends, family or pro players in this 4-4-2 formation.

GOALKEEPER
Ryan M

RIGHT DEFENDER
Jennifer

CENTRAL DEFENDER
ryan H

CENTRAL DEFENDER
omar
Sophi

LEFT DEFENDER
Noah

RIGHT MIDFIELDER
sophia omar
Daniel

CENTRAL MIDFIELDER
Edward

CENTRAL MIDFIELDER
Ben

LEFT MIDFIELDER
Katelyn

STRIKER
Max

STRIKER
daniel

Turn to the stickers at the back of the book and add the captain's armband sticker next to your skipper.

To finish your squad, choose your substitutes. Super subs can really change a game by giving teams an energy boost or replacing injured players.

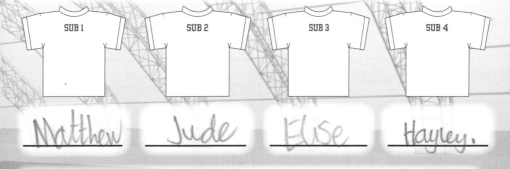

| SUB 1 | SUB 2 | SUB 3 | SUB 4 |

Matthew   Jude   Elise   Hayley.

The manager is in charge of picking which players, formations and tactics are needed to win each game. Who will you choose?

MANAGER

Ben

SOCCER SUDOKU

To solve this kickin' sudoku puzzle, you must fill every column, every row and every box with different pictures. It's as deadly as Beckham's right foot! Use your stickers to complete the grid.

REMEMBER: EACH PICTURE CAN ONLY APPEAR ONCE IN EACH, COLUMN, ROW AND BOX!

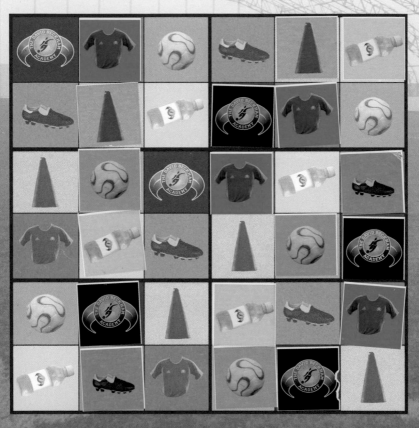

Answer:

A is for Academy . . .

Where you can learn skills from top coaches in an awesome arena.

B is for Ball . . .

Your new best friend. Take time out, just you and a ball, to improve your tricks and close control.

C is for Captain

Captains always help their team-mates and lead through actions, not just words. If the manager chooses you to be captain, it's a pretty big privilege.

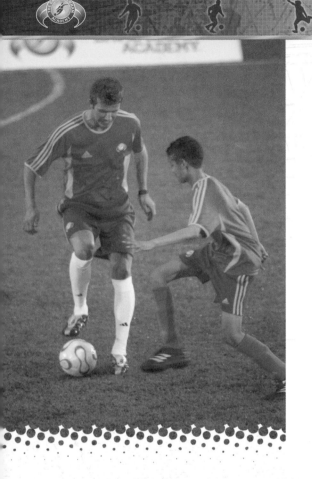

D
is for
Defender

Defenders love stopping goals going in as much as strikers love scoring them! Midfielders and Forwards need to help defend as a team, too.

 ## is for Energy

Pro players know that a healthy diet with five portions of fruit and veg every day will help them give 100% on the pitch.

F is for Free Kick

Practise, practise, practise, until you can bend it like Beckham! Vary your practice to include clever chips over the keeper and scorching shots!

G is for GOAL!!!

The aim of the game is to score more than your opponents. Although sometimes a narrow 1-0 victory over your closest rivals can feel as good as a 4-0 win!

H

is for Header

Tough-tackling defenders use their heads to clear the ball, and make contact with their foreheads for maximum control. Headed goals are a powerful weapon too.

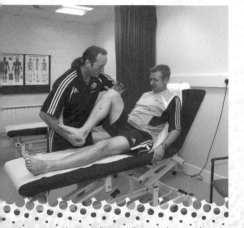

is for Injury

Team physios need more than a magic sponge in their kit bags! They carry all sorts of stuff to treat injuries that can happen on the pitch.

J is for Jog

Before you stretch your muscles, get your heart rate going by jogging for at least five minutes.

K is for Keepy-ups

All you need is a ball and you can practise your tricks and control pretty much anywhere. Use as many parts of your body as you can!

L

is for Legend

Over the years, Beckham has teamed up with players like Zinedine Zidane . . . pure class. And with over 100 caps for England we can safely say Beckham is in the legends category too.

M

is for Midfielder

Beckham's best position is in right midfield, where his pinpoint passes and explosive free kicks have won matches time and again.

N is for Net

Because there's no better feeling than seeing the net bulge when you score a gooaaall!

O is for One-on-one

Have confidence and keep super-chilled when you've only the 'keeper or last defender left to beat.

P is for Pitch

Pro teams use the whole of the pitch, including the wings on either side, to create space and open up the play.

Q is for Quick

Speed is an important skill. Learning to think fast is just as important as having quick feet.

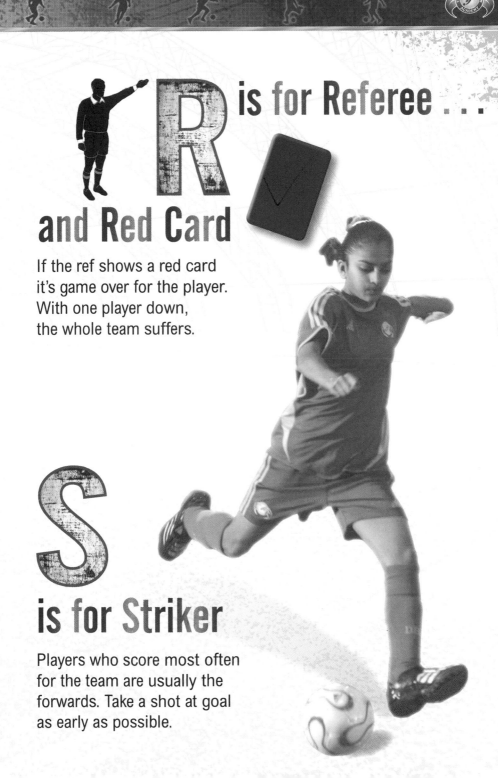

R is for Referee ...

and Red Card

If the ref shows a red card
it's game over for the player.
With one player down,
the whole team suffers.

S is for Striker

Players who score most often
for the team are usually the
forwards. Take a shot at goal
as early as possible.

T is for Team Talk

Talking to your team-
mates before, during
and after matches is
the best way to build
a winning team.

U is for Unbeatable

Building a good team
spirit and doing your
best will help you form
an unbeatable team.

V is for Visitors

Also known as the away team.
The home team always gets the
best dressing room!

W is for Warm-up and Warm-down

Start with some light running
before stretching your muscles
to keep injuries to a minimum.

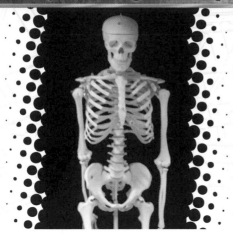

X
is for X-ray

Make sure you time your tackles properly to avoid broken bones!

Y
is for Yellow Card

Show the ref and fellow players respect and you should never be shown one of these.

Z
is for Zzzzs!

It is important to rest properly before and after games, so make sure you go to bed early to be match-fit the next morning!

FOOTBALL FOOD

Footy is a great game for keeping you fit, but to perform at your best, you need to eat the right foods too. This food wheel shows how to choose a balanced diet.

a. fruit and vegetables.

e. meat, fish and alternatives.

d. foods containing fats or sugar.

b. bread, other cereals and potatoes.

c. milk and dairy foods.

Use the wheel above to help you answer these questions. Write the letters in the boxes.

1. Which food groups should you eat most often?   **a b**

2. Which food group should you eat least often?   **d**

3. In which food group would you find cheese?   **c**

4. In which food group would you find eggs?   **e**

5. With which food group could you make a smoothie?   **a**

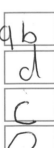

Answers: 1. a and b, 2. d, 3. c, 4. e, 5. a.

FIND 5-A-DAY

True pros rely on 5-a-day, every day, to give them their vitamins. That's 5 portions of different fruit and veg – juice and smoothies count, too. Look out for these words in the puzzle below. They could read from left to right, top to bottom or backwards.

X	F	J	R	Q	S	W	H	U	S
S	M	O	O	T	H	I	E	T	A
N	S	P	F	O	B	R	L	B	E
I	Q	O	Y	R	E	P	P	E	P
S	L	T	H	R	A	X	P	C	O
I	B	A	N	A	N	A	A	I	T
A	Q	T	X	C	S	D	Q	U	A
R	H	O	R	A	N	G	E	J	M
Y	T	L	K	F	B	O	I	F	O
J	W	E	C	U	T	T	E	L	T

- banana
- orange
- juice
- lettuce
- smoothie
- tomato
- pepper
- carrot
- beans
- apple
- raisins
- potato

STAY FLUID

It's massively important to drink lots of fluids, before, during and after playing sport. Feeling thirsty is your body's way of telling you you're dehydrated.

5 of these drinks are good choices. Colour them in on the football and put a cross through the one that you should rule out.

TRY TO DRINK

6 GLASSES OF WATER A DAY.

PHYSIO PUZZLE

The team physiotherapist, or physio for short, has a very important job. Take a guess which tasks they are in charge of. Tick the ones you think are right.

A physio . . .

☐ picks the team

☐ knows all about the human body

☐ treats injured players

☐ drives the team bus

☐ helps players prevent injuries

☐ buys and sells players

☐ waters the pitch

☐ measures players' heart rates

Answers: A physio DOES know all about the human body, treat injured players, help players prevent injuries and measure players' heart rates. A physio DOESN'T pick the team, drive the team bus, buy and sell players or water the pitch.

HEALTHY HEART

As you exercise your heart beats faster. Your heart rate is measured in beats per minute (bpm). Add the stickers for each activity below.

70 bpm

STANDING STILL

95 bpm

JOGGING

133 bpm

DRIBBLING

152 bpm

RUNNING WITH THE BALL

TRY MEASURING YOUR OWN HEART RATE TOO:
ask an adult to take your pulse after doing each activity above, using two fingers rather than their thumb. Count the number of beats in 1 minute.

MATCHDAY MENU

ACADEMY MENU

08:30
large glass of water
cereal and fruit

11:30
2 slices of toast and scrambled
eggs, tomatoes
fresh orange juice

14:00
sports drink or water (keep
taking sips until kick-off)
banana or raisins

15:00 **KICK-OFF!**

With a match to prepare for, Beckham and his team-mates need the right kind of fuel in their bodies to put in a good performance. Check out this top-tasting menu for some healthy meal ideas. The timings are a guide, adjust them to your own kick-off time.

ACADEMY MENU

15:45 — **HALF-TIME!** sports drink or water

17:00 — sports drink or water, banana or cereal bar

18:00 — soup and bread
chicken, pasta and vegetables
bananas and custard
large glass of diluted fruit juice or fruit squash

20:00 — 2 slices of toast and jam
large glass of diluted fruit juice or fruit squash

BOX DRILLS

Test your fitness with this tough box drill exercise. If you don't have cones to make a square, use jumpers or balls as markers.

START

Jog around the box twice to warm up.

Jockey (side-step) to the right, back to cone 1.

Sprint 5 metres to cone 2.

REPEAT THE DRILL

5 TIMES

MAKING SURE YOU ARE FULLY RECOVERED BEFORE STARTING EACH CIRCUIT.

JOG AND SKIP

2 TIMES

ROUND THE SQUARE TO HELP FULL RECOVERY.

4

Backpedal 5 metres to cone 4, make sharp right cut.

3

Jockey to the left 5 metres to cone 3.

YOU COULD TRY DRIBBLING WITH A BALL AROUND THE SQUARE, TOO.

GO FOR GOAL!

You've hit a cone. Go back to the start.

You've finished your warm-up, run on 2 spaces.

A smoothie gives you an energy boost, sprint forwards 4 spaces.

A great night's sleep leaves you raring to go – run on 2 spaces.

START

Play this game with a team-mate. You'll need a dice, and a counter each. Take it in turns to throw the dice and move around the board. The first player to score wins!

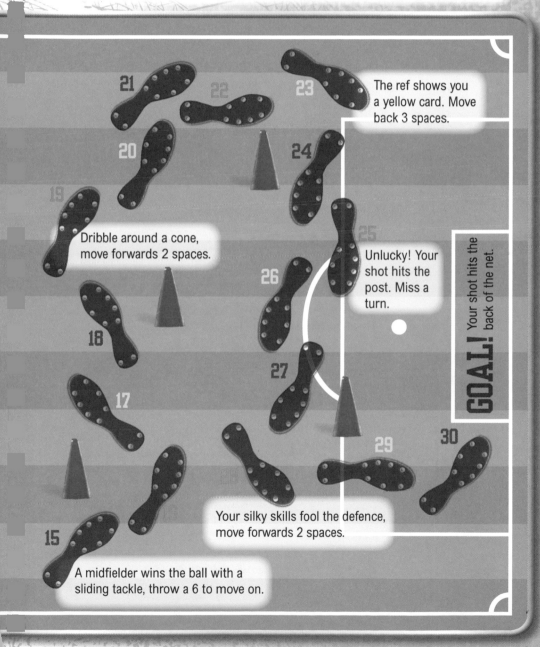

21

22

23

The ref shows you a yellow card. Move back 3 spaces.

20

24

19

Dribble around a cone, move forwards 2 spaces.

25

Unlucky! Your shot hits the post. Miss a turn.

26

18

27

GOAL! Your shot hits the back of the net.

17

30

29

Your silky skills fool the defence, move forwards 2 spaces.

15

A midfielder wins the ball with a sliding tackle, throw a 6 to move on.

KIT BAG

Make sure your kit fits so you feel comfortable and perform at your best in all weather conditions.

Wear an extra layer, like a training top, until you're properly warmed up.

Short sleeves are great for keeping cool in warmer weather.

A good pair of boots should last you ages and give your feet great protection.

Beckham wore these Predator boots when he netted for Man Utd from the half-way line!

THE WARM-UP

Warming up is vital before training and matches to prepare your body and mind. Don't forget to warm down, too (repeat the warm-up). Start with some light running, then, slowly build up your speed to include some short sprints. Next, work on these muscle groups, holding each stretch for ten seconds.

STRETCH OUT YOUR . . .

NECK
gently from side to side to help your heading.

HIPS
for when you twist and turn with the ball.

GROIN AREA
for when you change direction quickly or land awkwardly following a tackle.

HAMSTRINGS
for when you accelerate away with or without the ball.

CALVES
to build lower-leg strength for all-round play.

QUADS
to reduce injuries when striking the ball.

WITH THE WARM-UP OVER, YOU'RE READY TO WORK ON YOUR SKILLS.

BALL CONTROL

Learning to control the ball well affects every move you make on the pitch. As with every skill, you'll get better the more you practise. Work hard and make the ball your new best friend!

When you've tried each skill, add a sticker football to the icon below.

Practise juggling the ball: start by using either or both feet and allow yourself one bounce of the ball in between touches. Try to use fewer bounces until you can juggle successfully without any bounces at all. As you feel more confident, try to cushion the ball using your head, chest and thighs.

Place a sticker here.

Your first touch is the most important: a good first touch gives you more time.

LONG PASS

Picking out a team-mate on the other side of the pitch is a top skill to practise. Use your judgement and look around you to see if the long pass is the best option. Is there an easier, shorter ball?

A decent long pass will get defenders in a spin and can quickly turn defence into attack. Keeping your eyes firmly on the ball, lean back slightly and strike it on its lower half. This will give the ball elevation and pace. Long passes are spectacular when they come off, but can be tricky.

Hit your long pass into space: your team-mate will be on the move and can run on to the ball.

Place a sticker here

CHIPPED BALL

The chipped shot or pass can be a deadly weapon, to trouble the goalie or to keep possession for the team when you find yourself in a tight space.

When chipping a pass, meet the ball straight-on. With your striking foot, stab the bottom of the ball where it meets the ground. This will create backspin and send the ball sailing into the air and over the defender or keeper's head.

Practise your chipped passes with a team-mate to become an expert at this technique!

Place a stick...

DEFENDING

Defending is more than just tackling and heading. Clever defenders, from full-backs to centre-halves, know exactly when to make their move to stop the other team scoring.

When trying to win back possession, the same rules apply whether the ball is on the ground or in the air: close down the attacking player so they don't have space to do their job, time your challenge properly to win the ball cleanly and be patient — force the other player to make a mistake.

Don't dive in when making a tackle: staying on your feet will help you remain in control.

Place a sticker here

DRIBBLING

This is something you can practise on your own. Set off, moving with the ball close to your feet. Take plenty of touches to keep the ball firmly under control.

Keep your head up, so you can see oncoming defenders and where to direct your pass.

When you feel confident dribbling with the ball, practise changing speed and direction and using different parts of the foot to move the ball.

Brazil have loads of top dribblers, Beckham's old team-mate at Madrid, Robinho, is a wizard on the wing.

Place a sticker here

HEADING

Heading the ball is a vital skill – whatever your playing position. Keeping your eyes on the ball, make contact with your forehead.

Place a sticker here

For defensive headers, aim to head the ball high and away from goal. Just watch Beckham's England team-mate John Terry to see how it's done.

The key to attacking headers is to try to head downwards, so make sure you get over the ball and face the target after contact.

England ace Frank Lampard is brilliant in the box at this move.

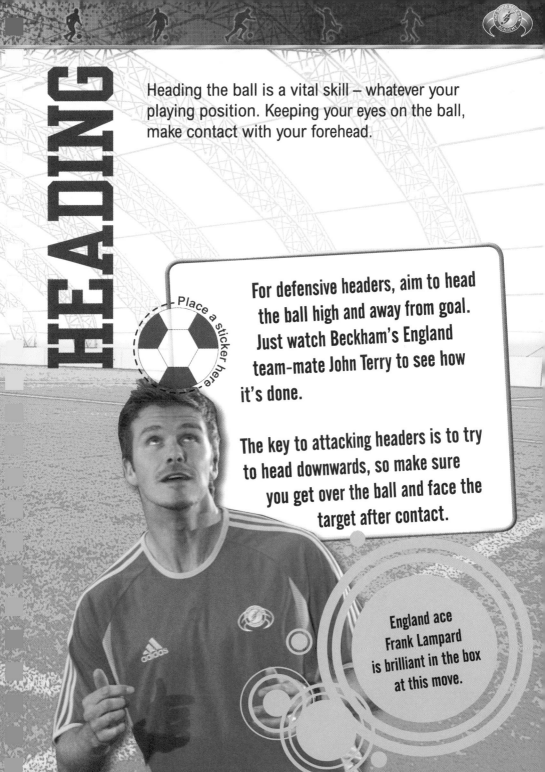

ONE-ON-ONE

One-on-one is when you find yourself running at goal with only the 'keeper or last defender to beat. Attacking players will find themselves in this position most often.

This skill is all about instinct and confidence — you've got to believe you're going to score every time. In a goal-scoring position, the goalie will stay on their feet as long as possible — don't panic. Running at pace, try two techniques — chipping and dribbling around the 'keeper.

With this move, the trick is to stay cool. Use your eyes to kid the 'keeper into going the wrong way.

Place a sticker here.

FREE KICKS

Throughout his career, Beckham has proved he's in a class of his own when it comes to taking free kicks. He's scored some scorchers in massive matches for both club and country.

Approaching the ball from an angle, take a good long run up. Plant the non-striking foot firmly on the ground and lean back slightly to get the ball up and over the wall.
Wrap the inside of your striking foot around the ball to create some swerve. Follow through with the same foot to get plenty of pace on the ball and bend it like Beckham!

Your team-mates can help confuse the opposition by getting in the wall, and in the 'keeper's way!

Place a sticker here

PENALTIES

From the moment the penalty is awarded,
it's important to keep your cool. Try to block out
everything around you and take a deep breath.

Decide where you're going to put the
ball and don't change your mind.
Be sure to concentrate on the ball
as you take the kick.

A well-directed, firmly struck
penalty is almost impossible for
the goalkeeper to save.

Beckham's
best penalty was in
the 2002 World Cup
finals: scoring the spot-
kick helped England
beat Argentina!

Place a sticker here

SHOOTING

Football is all about scoring goals. If you don't shoot, you don't score, so when you find yourself in a goal-scoring position remember these tips . . .

Have a quick look to see if the 'keeper has left a gap on either side. Choose the right technique — sidefoot for accuracy or use the instep (laces) and follow through for power.

When you take the strike, keep your head down and your eyes on the ball

Try to make a clean contact with the ball and stay relaxed.

Place a sticker here

ACADEMY ACE!

Once you've mastered the moves in this section, tick off each skill on our handy Academy checklist.

I CAN . . .

warm up properly	✓
control the ball well, using both feet	✓
find a team-mate with a long pass	✗
chip a ball to get out of trouble	✗
defend as part of a team	✗
dribble confidently past defenders	✗
head the ball, in defence and attack	✗
keep cool in a one-to-one situation	✓
test the 'keeper with a free kick	✓
take a penalty with confidence	✓
get a shot on target, when in front of goal	✓

Signed:

Edward

CAPTAIN

Use these stickers with the Soccer Sudoku puzzle.